My Day

written by Anne Giulieri

illustrated by Wesley Lowe

My name is Beth and I'm 10.

This is my mum and this is my dad.

I have a brother and a sister, too.

2

In my bedroom I have lots of books.
I also have a desk and a bed.

This is my *wheelchair*.

It helps me to *move* around.

I bring my books to school in my bag.

My bag is always on the side of my wheelchair.

My mum puts me in the van to go to school.

At school, my mum gets me out of the van.

My school has *ramps* so that I can go
from the playground to my *classroom*.
Some of my friends *wave* to me
as I go to my classroom.
Some of my friends run over to me, too.

We do our *schoolwork* at our *tables*.

I sit at the orange table with my friends.

We have *story-time* on the *floor*.
My teacher always lets a friend
sit on a *chair* next to me.

I like to play outside with my friends.

We have a secret tree

that we like to play under.

My friends can help to push my chair, too.

I like to play with a ball at *sports-time.*

My teacher tells me that I'm very good at *sport.*

At night-time I go to bed and read.
Then I go to sleep and *dream*
of all the things I will do at school.

Picture Glossary

chair

move

sports-time

wheelchair

classroom

ramps

story-time

dream

schoolwork

tables

floor

sport

wave